WOLFGANG AMADEUS MOZART

SYMPHONY No. 38

D Major/D-Dur/Ré majeur

K504

"Prague"

D1744487

Ernst Eulenburg Ltd

London · Mainz · Madrid · New York · Paris · Tokyo · Toronto · Zürich

CONTENTS/INHALT/TABLE

The present edition of Mozart's Symphony No.38, K504, has been re-set from the former Eulenburg edition (plate number E.E.3635) by Theodor Kroyer (1873–1945) dated Leipzig, Autumn 1931. Kroyer's edition (based on his readings of the autograph MSS and early printed editions) has been re-checked and corrected where necessary from the relevant texts published in the *NMA*.

Ernst Eulenburg Ltd
48 Great Marlborough Street
London W1F 7BB

PREFACE

For three years after the composition of the 'Linz' Symphony (November 1783) Mozart wrote no symphonies but produced a remarkable series of works, among them the last four of the six string quartets he was to dedicate to Haydn in 1785, a dozen piano concertos from K449 to K503, various concert arias and sonatas, the *Masonic Funeral Music*, *The Impresario*, and *The Marriage of Figaro*. The latter was first produced in Vienna on 1 May 1786 and was enthusiastically received only to be replaced after only nine performances by the popular success of Martin y Soler's *Una cosa rara*, not to be heard again in the Austrian capital for another two years. It was the Italian opera company of Pasquale Bondini in Prague that took up *Figaro* with such success in late 1786 that the opera saved the company from near bankruptcy and Mozart was invited to Prague to hear their production.[1]

Soon after Mozart and Constanze arrived in Prague on 15 January 1787, Wolfgang wrote to his Vienna friend, Baron Gottfried von Jacquin: 'I must frankly admit that, although I meet with all possible courtesies and honours here and although Prague is indeed a very beautiful and pleasant place, I long most ardently to be back in Vienna [. . .] My concert is to take place in the theatre on Friday, the 19th, and I shall probably have to give a second one, which unfortunately will prolong my stay here.'[2] It must be admitted

that these sentiments were less to do with Mozart's love of Vienna, which was now losing interest in him, but with the furtherance of his desire to move to England where he felt that there would be a greater chance of achieving the degree of long-term financial stability that had eluded him in Vienna. The English plan never came to fruition.

On 17 January Mozart attended a performance of *Figaro* and a few days later conducted a performance himself. His own concert on the 19th was enthusiastically received not only for his piano playing but for the first performance of a new symphony in D major, completed in Vienna on 6 December 1786, no doubt with the trip to Prague in mind. The symphony (No. 38, K504) is now known by the name of that city and the first performance was recalled in the biography of Mozart written some 11 years later by Franz Niemetschek, a Prague schoolmaster and friend of the composer who after Mozart's death took on the responsibility of educating his seven-year-old son, Carl: '[...] the grand symphony in D major', wrote Niemetschek, 'which is still always a favourite in Prague, although it has no doubt been heard a hundred times.'[3] What with *Figaro* and the new Symphony, the trip to Prague had been eminently worthwhile and when Mozart returned to Vienna in February he had

[1] H.C.Robbins Landon, *Mozart – The Golden Years* (London, 1989/1990), pp166, 167

[2] Emily Anderson, *The Letters of Mozart and his Family* (London, 1938; 3rd edn., London, 1985), Letter 544, p904

[3] Neal Zaslaw, *Mozart's Symphonies: Context, Performance Practice, Reception* (Oxford, 1989/91), p411, citing Franz Niemetschek, *Leben des K.K. Kapellmeisters Wolfgang Gottlieb Mozart, nach Originalquellen beschrieben* (Prague, 1798); transl. Helen Mautner as: *Life of Mozart* (London, 1956), pp33, 35–7

with him a contract for a new opera which was to become *Don Giovanni*.

The 'Prague' Symphony occupies a special place in Mozart's output, displaying new dimensions of mood, technique, orchestration (notably a heightened awareness of the soloistic capabilities of the winds, already evident in the piano concertos K482 and K491) and general character, in the latter respect looking forward to *Don Giovanni*. It must be ranked with the last three great symphonies in terms of sheer quality of inspiration, just as Haydn's 'Oxford' Symphony (No.92), for the same reason, belongs with the 12 'London' Symphonies which crowned that composer's symphonic achievement. The gravity and expansiveness of the slow introduction; the mysterious emergence from it of the *Allegro*; the contrapuntal wizardry of the development; the richness of harmonic resource especially evident in the *Andante* (the finest of the three siciliano-type movements that started with the 'Paris' Symphony (1778) – developed further in the 'Linz' Symphony (1783), reaching a climax in this expressive and stately dance); the powerful, yet fleet-footed final *Presto* (the opening figure of which reminds one of the beginning of the Susanna/Cherubino duet, 'Aprite, presto' from Act II of *Figaro*), all signal the advent of a new Mozart at the threshold of a new phase of creative development.

The 'Prague' Symphony, like the 'Paris' Symphony, has no minuet, but whereas the earlier omission was in accordance with French custom, no such consideration applies here. Neither did Mozart feel the need (or have the time) to add one later as he had done with the Symphony No. 33, K319. It is more likely that there was simply no place for a minuet in his scheme for the work.

Interestingly, an essay, 'Concerning Minuets in Symphonies', was published in 1791–2 by Court Counsellor Johann Gottlieb Carl Spazier in which he writes:

'[...] I consider minuets effective [...] only as long as they in no way at all inopportunely remind one of the *dance floor* and of the misuse of music. And if they are caricatured – as is often the case with Haydn and Pleyel – they cause *laughter*, in which case there can no longer be any question of whether minuets are admissible in noble symphonies, which are fiery and therefore stormy, or which should put us in a festive mood. But even when that is not the case, the substance of minuets is *too insignificant*, which only disrupts or halts entirely the symphony's continuity and momentum.'[4]

The autograph score of the 'Prague' Symphony is one of the many rare treasures that was moved, during World War II, from the Preußische Staatsbibliothek in Berlin to Silesia for safety. It is now housed in the Jagellonian University Library in Cracow.

Harry Newstone

[4] Zaslaw, ibid., p416. Zaslaw's excerpt from Spazier's essay, which he mildy characterizes as 'conservative', in that 'he [Spazier] clings to the baroque aesthetic theory of the unity of affect within single movements, and even to some extent across all the movements of a symphony', is considerably more comprehensive than our short extract shows. It is ironic, too, that Spazier's tilt at Haydn was made before he can have known the 'London' Symphonies in which series the minuet is transformed from a dance movement to one of truly symphonic weight and proportions. Spazier: 'Über Menuetten in Sinfonien', Musikalisches Wochenblatt (1791–2), 91–2. transl. Willard Daetsch. Original repr. H-G Ottenberg (ed), *Der critische Musicus an der Spree. Berliner Musikschriftum von 1748 bis 1799: Eine Dokumentation* (Leipzig, 1984), 318–20.

VORWORT

Nach der Komposition der "Linzer" Sinfonie (November 1783) schrieb Mozart zwar drei Jahre lang keine Sinfonien mehr, aber er schuf eine Reihe anderer bemerkenswerter Werke, unter anderem die letzten vier der sechs Streichquartette, die er 1785 Haydn widmen sollte, sowie ein Dutzend Klavierkonzerte von KV449 bis KV503, diverse Konzertarien und Sonaten, die *Maurerische Trauermusik*, den *Schauspieldirektor* und *Le nozze di Figaro*. Das letztgenannte Werk war zum ersten Mal am 1. Mai 1786 in Wien auf der Bühne zu erleben und fand beim Publikum großen Anklang. Allerdings wurde es nach nur neun Aufführungen abgesetzt und mit einer Inszenierung von Martin y Solers beliebtem Stück *Una cosa rara* ersetzt. Zwei Jahre dauerte es, bis der *Figaro* in der österreichischen Hauptstadt wieder zu hören war. Unterdessen nahm sich das italienische Opernunternehmen von Pasquale Bondini in Prag gegen Ende 1786 des *Figaros* mit solchem Erfolg an, dass dadurch das Unternehmen vor dem Bankrott gerettet wurde und Mozart eine Einladung nach Prag erhielt, um dieser Inszenierung beizuwohnen.[1]

Kurz nach seiner und Constanzes Ankunft in Prag am 15. Januar 1787 schrieb Mozart an seinen Wiener Freund, den Baron Gottfried von Jacquin: „Ich muß ihnen aufrichtig gestehen, daß |: obwohl ich hier alle mögliche höflichkeiten und Ehren genüsse, und Prag in der That ein sehr schöner und angenehmer ort ist :| ich mich doch recht sehr wieder nach Wienn sehne [...] künftigen freytag, den 19:ten wird meine academie im theater seyn; ich werde vermuthlich eine zwote geben müssen; das wird meinen aufenthalt hier *leider* verlängern."[2] Diese Gesinnung hatte wohl weniger mit Mozarts Liebe der Stadt Wien zu tun, die mittlerweile zunehmend weniger Interesse an Mozart zeigte, sondern mit der Erfüllung seines Wunsches, nach England zu ziehen, wo er glaubte, eine bessere Chance zu haben, ein Maß an längerfristiger finanzieller Stabilität zu erreichen, das ihm in Wien nicht möglich war. Der England-Plan ging nie in Erfüllung.

Am 17. Januar besuchte Mozart eine Aufführung des *Figaros*, und ein paar Tage später dirigierte er selber eine Aufführung. Sein eigenes Konzert am 19. Januar wurde mit Begeisterung aufgenommen, nicht nur aufgrund seines Klavierspiels, sondern auch wegen der Uraufführung einer neuen Sinfonie in D-Dur, die Mozart am 6. Dezember 1786 in Wien abgeschlossen hatte, zweifellos mit dem Gedanken an seine bevorstehende Reise nach Prag. Die Sinfonie (Nr. 38, KV504) ist heute unter dem Namen dieser Stadt bekannt. Die Uraufführung wurde in der ungefähr elf Jahre später geschriebenen Mozartbiographie von Franz Niemetschek, einem Prager Schulmeister und Freund des Komponisten, der nach Mozarts Tod die Verantwortung für die Ausbildung seines siebenjährigen Sohns Carl übernahm, beschrieben. Die große Sinfonie in D-Dur sei „noch immer ein Lieblingsstück des Prager Publikums [...]",

---

[1] H. C. Robbins Landon, *Mozart – The Golden Years* (London 1989/1990), S. 166, 167

[2] Wilhelm A. Bauer, Otto E. Deutsch, *Mozart: Briefe und Aufzeichnungen*, Gesamtausgabe, Bd. IV (Kassel 1962–75), S. 10, 11

schrieb Niemetschek, „obschon sie wohl hundertmal gehört ward".[3] Angesichts des Erfolgs des *Figaros* und der neuen Sinfonie erwies sich die Reise nach Prag allemal der Mühe wert, und als Mozart im Februar nach Wien zurückkehrte, trug er einen Vertrag für eine neue Oper bei sich, die als *Don Giovanni* Gestalt annehmen sollte.

Die „Prager" Sinfonie nimmt eine besondere Stellung im Schaffen Mozarts ein. Sie offenbart neue Dimensionen der Stimmung, Technik, Orchestrierung (besonders ein geschärftes Bewusstsein für das solistische Potential der Holzbläser, das schon in den Klavierkonzerten KV482 und KV491 deutlich wurde) und des allgemeinen, auf den *Don Giovanni* vorausweisenden Charakters. Hinsichtlich der außerordentlichen Qualität der Einfälle ist die „Prager" Sinfonie den letzten drei großen Sinfonien zweifellos ebenbürtig, genau wie Haydns „Oxford"-Sinfonie (Nr. 92) aus demselben Grund den zwölf, sein sinfonisches Schaffen krönenden „Londoner" Sinfonien gleichgestellt werden kann. Die Gesetztheit und Länge der langsamen Einleitung, das mysteriöse Erscheinen des Allegros aus dieser Einleitung, die kontrapunktischen Kunststücke der Durchführung, der Reichtum der harmonischen Mittel, die besonders im Andante zum Tragen kommen – der feinste der drei Siziliano-artigen Sätze, die in der „Pariser" Sinfonie (1778) ihren Anfang genommen hatten, in der „Linzer" Sinfonie (1783) weiterentwickelt wurden und in diesem ausdrucksstarken

und erhabenen Tanz einen Höhepunkt erreichten – sowie das gewaltige und doch geschwinde Presto (dessen einleitendes Motiv an den Anfang des Duetts „Aprite, presto" zwischen Susanna und Cherubino aus dem II. Akt des *Figaros* erinnert), all das kündigt die Ankunft eines neuen Mozart an der Schwelle zu einer neuen Phase seiner künstlerischen Entwicklung an.

Die „Prager" Sinfonie hat wie die „Pariser" Sinfonie kein Menuett. Wo dort eine Rechtfertigung in der Befolgung französischer Gebräuche gegeben ist, gilt das im Falle der „Prager Sinfonie" nicht. Mozart sah sich auch nicht genötigt (noch hatte er die Zeit), ein Menuett später hinzuzufügen, wie er es noch mit seiner Sinfonie Nr. 33, KV319 getan hatte. Wahrscheinlich ist eher, dass es in seinem Werkkonzept einfach keinen Platz für ein Menuett gab. Interessanterweise erschien 1791–1792 ein Aufsatz vom Hofberater Johann Gottlieb Carl Spazier mit dem Titel „Über Menuetten in Sinfonien", in dem jener schrieb:

„Sodann halte ich die Menuetten darum für effektwidrig, weil sie, wenn sie glattweg in dieser Form gearbeitet sind, schlechterdings zur Unzeit an den *Tanzboden* und an den Mißbrauch der Musik erinnern; und, sind sie karrikaturirt – wie dies mit Haydn'schen und Pleyel'schen öfters der Fall ist – das *Lachen* erregen. Ist das letztere, so kann es keine Frage mehr seyn, ob Menuetten bei edlen Sinfonien, die feurig daher stürmen, oder uns in ein feierliches Gefühl versetzen sollen, zuverlässig sind. Aber auch das alles nicht genommen, so sind sie gar zu *kleine Massen*, die, ohne alle Veranlassung und Vorbereitung zwischen durch geworfen werden, und wel-

[3] Neal Zaslaw, *Mozart's Symphonies, Context, Performance Practice, Reception* (Oxford, 1989/91), S. 411, zitiert Franz Niemetschek, *Leben des K. K. Kapellmeisters Wolfgang Gottlieb Mozart, nach Originalquellen beschrieben* (Prag 1798); übersetzt von H. Mautner als: *Life of Mozart* (London 1956), S. 33, 35–7

che das Stetige und Fortströmende der Sinfonie nur stören und aufhalten".[4]

Die Autographpartitur der „Prager" Sinfonie ist einer der vielen seltenen Schätze, die im Zweiten Weltkrieg aus der Preußischen Staatsbibliothek zu Berlin nach Schlesien zur Sicherheit ausgelagert wurden. Die Partitur befindet sich heute in der Jagellonischen Universitätsbibliothek in Kraków.

Harry Newstone
Übersetzung: Elke Hockings

---

[4] Neal Zaslaw, ibid, S. 416 Zaslaws Ausschnitt aus Spaziers Aufsatz, den er mild als „konservativ" kritisierte, weil „er [Spazier] an der barocken Ästhetik festhält, die die Einheit eines Affekts innerhalb eines Satzes, und bis zu einem gewissen Grad für alle Sätze einer Sinfonie, fordert", ist erheblich länger als unser kurzer Ausschnitt zeigt. Es wundert auch, dass Spaziers abwertende Bemerkung gegenüber Haydn geäußert wurde, bevor Spazier die „Londoner" Sinfonien gekannt haben konnte, in denen das Menuett von einem Tanzsatz zu einem Satz mit wirklich sinfonischen Ausmaßen und Gewichtung verwandelt wurde. Spazier, „Über Menuetten in Sinfonien", Musikalisches Wochenblatt (1791–1792), S. 91–92. übersetzt von Willard Daetsch. Orig. Repr. H.-G. Ottenberg (ed.), *Der critische Musicus an der Spree. Berliner Musikschriftum von 1748 bis 1799: Eine Dokumentation* (Leipzig 1984), S. 318–20.

PRÉFACE

Au cours des trois années qui suivirent la composition de la Symphonie « Linz » (novembre 1783), Mozart ne composa pas de symphonie mais produisit une série remarquable d'œuvres parmi lesquelles figurent les quatre derniers des six quatuors dédiés à Haydn en 1785, douze concertos pour piano, du K.449 au K.503, divers airs de concert et sonates, la *Marche funèbre maçonnique (Maurerische Trauermusik)*, le Singspiel *Le directeur de théâtre (Der Schauspieldirektor)* et l'opéra *Les noces de Figaro (Le nozze di Figaro)*. Ce dernier fut créé à Vienne le 1er mai 1786 mais, en dépit de l'accueil enthousiaste qu'il reçut, fut retiré de l'affiche après neuf représentations seulement et remplacé par le succès populaire *Una cosa rara* de Martin y Soler, pour ne plus être donné dans la capitale autrichienne pendant les deux années qui suivirent. La troupe d'opéra italienne de Pasquale Bondini, établie à Prague, reprit *Les noces* fin 1786 et obtint un tel triomphe que la troupe fut sauvée de la banqueroute qui la menaçait et que Mozart fut invité à Prague pour assister à sa production. [1]

Peu après l'arrivée de Mozart et de Constanze à Prague, le 15 janvier 1787, Wolfgang écrivit à son ami le baron Gottfried von Jacquin à Vienne : « Je dois avouer franchement que, malgré l'accueil plein de courtoisie et d'honneurs que je reçois ici et en dépit de la grande beauté et de l'agrément de la ville de Prague, j'ai la plus ardente envie de retourner à Vienne [...] Mon concert aura lieu au théâtre le vendredi 19 et je devrais probablement en donner un autre, ce qui malheureusement prolongera mon séjour ici. » [2] Il faut bien admettre que ces sentiments étaient moins suscités par l'attachement de Mozart à Vienne, dont l'intérêt pour lui s'amenuisait, que par la poursuite de son désir de s'installer en Angleterre où il pensait avoir de plus grandes chances de trouver la stabilité financière durable qui lui avait échappé à Vienne. Ses projets anglais ne se réalisèrent jamais.

Le 17 janvier, Mozart assista à une représentation des *Noces* et, quelques jours plus tard, en dirigea lui-même une représentation. Son propre concert du 19 janvier reçut un accueil enthousiaste réservé non seulement à son interprétation au piano mais également à la création d'une nouvelle symphonie en *ré* majeur, achevée à Vienne le 6 décembre 1786 et manifestement écrite en vue du voyage à Prague. Cette symphonie (n°38, K.504) est depuis connue par le nom de la ville dans laquelle eut lieu sa création, relatée quelques onze années plus tard dans la biographie de Mozart par Franz Niemetschek, maître d'école praguois ami du compositeur qui, à la mort de Mozart, prit la responsabilité de l'éducation de son fils Carl, âgé de sept ans : «[...] la grande symphonie en *ré* majeur », écrit-il « qui demeure une des œuvres favorites à Prague, bien qu'on l'y ait entendue, sans doute, cent fois » [3]. Le voyage à

[1] H.C. Robbin Landon, *Mozart – The Golden Years*, Londres, 1989/1990, pp.166–167

[2] Emily Anderson, *The Letters of Mozart and his Family*, Londres, 1938; Londres 1985³, lettre 544, pp.904

[3] Neal Zaslaw, *Mozart's Symphonies, Context, Performance, Practice, Reception*, Oxford, 1989/91, p. 411, citant Franz Niemetschek, *Leben des*

Prague, qui vit le succès des *Noces* et la création de la nouvelle symphonie, se révéla hautement profitable et Mozart repartit pour Vienne en février emportant le contrat pour un nouvel opéra qui aboutirait à *Don Giovanni*.

La Symphonie « Prague » occupe une place spéciale dans la production de Mozart du fait de la nouvelle envergure qu'elle accorde à l'expression, à la technique, à l'orchestration (en particulier par la conscience accrue des capacités solistes des instruments à vent qui se profilait déjà dans les concertos pour piano K.482 et K.491) et au caractère général de l'œuvre qui s'oriente vers celui de *Don Giovanni*. Elle se place au niveau des trois dernières grandes symphonies quant à la qualité absolue de son inspiration, de même que la Symphonie « Oxford » de Haydn (No 92), pour les mêmes raisons, s'aligne sur les 12 symphonies « Londoniennes » qui couronnent l'œuvre symphonique de ce compositeur. La gravité et l'étendue de l'introduction lente dont émerge mystérieusement l'*Allegro*, la complexité contrapuntique du développement, la richesse harmonique, notamment dans l'*Andante* (le plus beau des trois mouvements en forme de sicilienne dont le premier remonte à la Symphonie « Parisienne » (1778) et que l'on retrouve dans la Symphonie « Linz » (1783), qui atteint ici l'apogée de cette danse expressive et imposante), le *Presto* final alliant puissance et prestesse (dont le début rappelle celui du duo entre Suzanne et Chérubin « Aprite, presto » de l'acte II de *Noces de Figaro*), tous ces aspects annoncent l'avènement d'un

Mozart au seuil d'une nouvelle phase de développement créatif.

La Symphonie « Prague », à l'image de la Symphonie « Parisienne », ne comporte pas de menuet, omission qui pouvait correspondre à l'usage français mais qui ne se justifie pas ici. Mozart ne ressentit d'ailleurs pas le besoin (ou n'eut pas le temps) d'en ajouter un par la suite comme il l'avait fait pour la Symphonie n°33, K.319. Il paraît plus probable qu'un menuet n'avait pas sa place dans le schéma conçu par Mozart pour cette œuvre. Il est intéressant de lire ce qu'écrivit le Conseiller à la Cour Johann Gottlieb Carl Spazier dans un essai publié en 1791/92, intitulé *Des menuets dans les symphonies* :

« [...] Je considère que les menuets font leur effet [...] s'ils ne rappellent pas inopportunément le *bal* ni le détournement de la musique. S'ils sont caricaturés – comme souvent chez Haydn et Pleyel – ils déchaînent le *rire* et, dans ce cas, il ne peut être question de leur congruité dans les symphonies nobles, tumultueuses et, donc, orageuses ou dans celles qui doivent mettre dans une ambiance de liesse. Toutefois, même si ce n'est pas le cas, la substance du menuet est *trop insignifiante* et ne fait que troubler ou rompre complètement la continuité et l'élan de la symphonie. » [4]

[4] Neal Zaslaw, *ibid.*, p.416. L'extrait tiré par Zaslaw de l'essai de Spazier, qu'il qualifie avec bienveillance de « conservateur » parce qu' « il [Spazier] adhère à la théorie esthétique baroque d'unité d'affect à l'intérieur de chaque mouvement, étendue, dans une certaine mesure, à tous les mouvements d'une symphonie », est considérablement plus complet que ne le montre notre courte citation. Il est également curieux de noter que la réflexion de Spazier sur Haydn a été formulée avant qu'il ait pu avoir connaissance de la série des Symphonies « Londoniennes » dans laquelle le menuet se mue d'un mouvement de danse à un mouvement d'ampleur et de proportions authentiquement symphoniques. Spazier,

K.K. *Kapellmeister Wolfang Gottlieb Mozart, nach Originalquellen beschrieben*, Prague, 1798, traduction anglaise de Helen Mautner : *Life of Mozart*, Londres, 1956, pp.33, 35–37

La partition autographe de la Symphonie « Prague » est l'un des nombreux trésors rares qui furent déplacés pendant la seconde guerre mondiale de la Preussische Staatsbibliothek de Berlin vers la Silésie pour plus de sûreté. Elle est actuellement conservée à la bibliothèque de l'Université Jagellonian de Cracovie.

Harry Newstone
Traduction: Agnès Ausseur

Über Menuetten in Sinfonien in : *Musikalisches Wochenblatt* (1791–92), 91–2, traduction anglaise Willard Daetsch. Reprographie des originaux : H-G Ottenberg (éditeur), *Der critische Musicus an der Spree. Berliner Musikschriftum von 1748 bis 1799 : Eine Dokumentation*, Leipzig, 1984, pp.318–320.

SYMPHONY No. 38

Wolfgang Amadeus Mozart
(1756–1791)
K504

I. Adagio

2

4

8

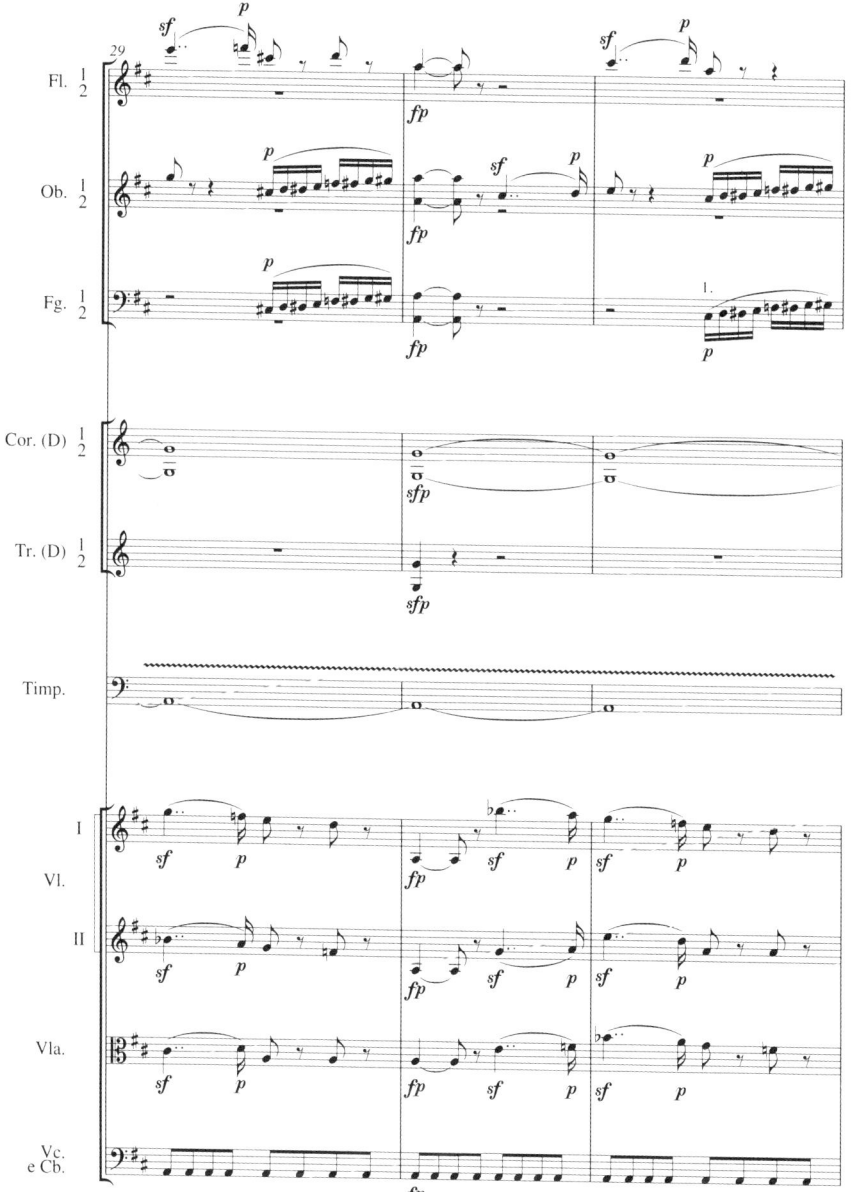

10

EE 7092

12

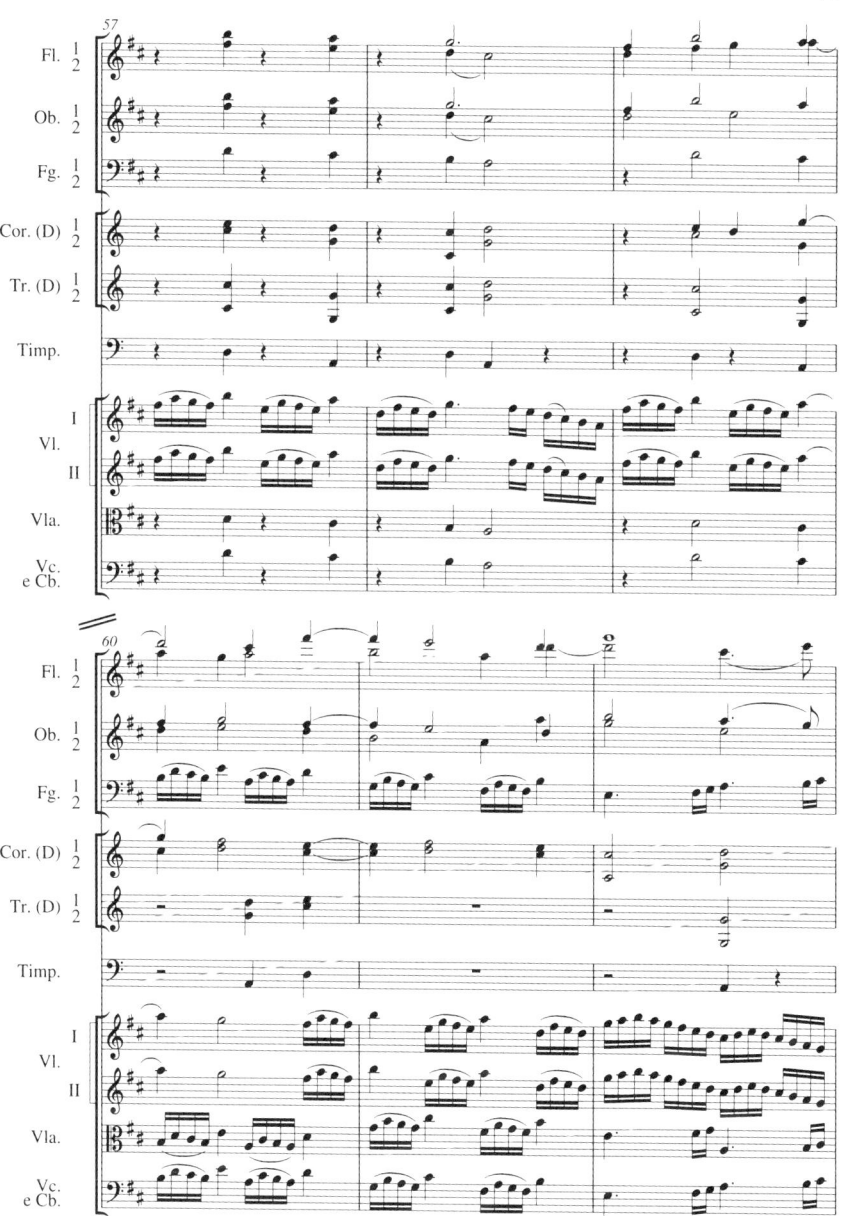

16

18

20

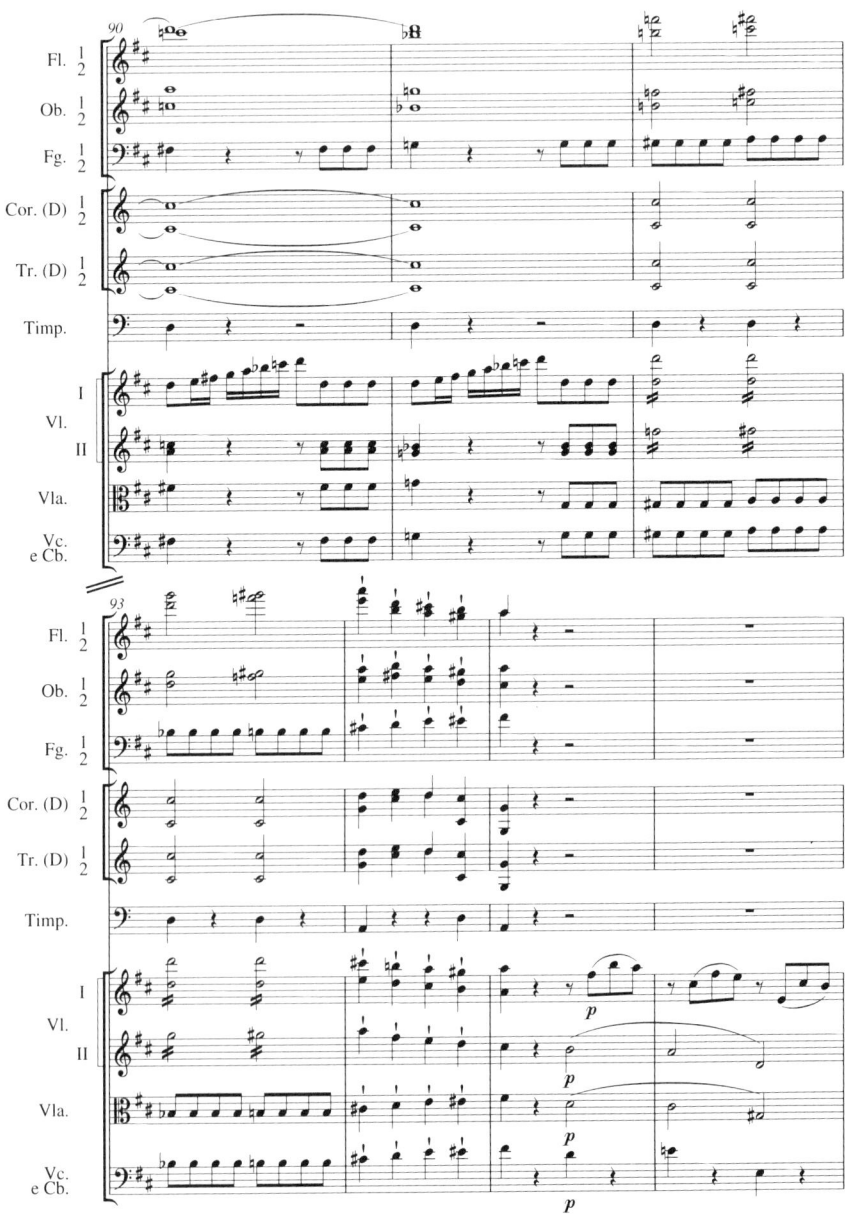

22

24

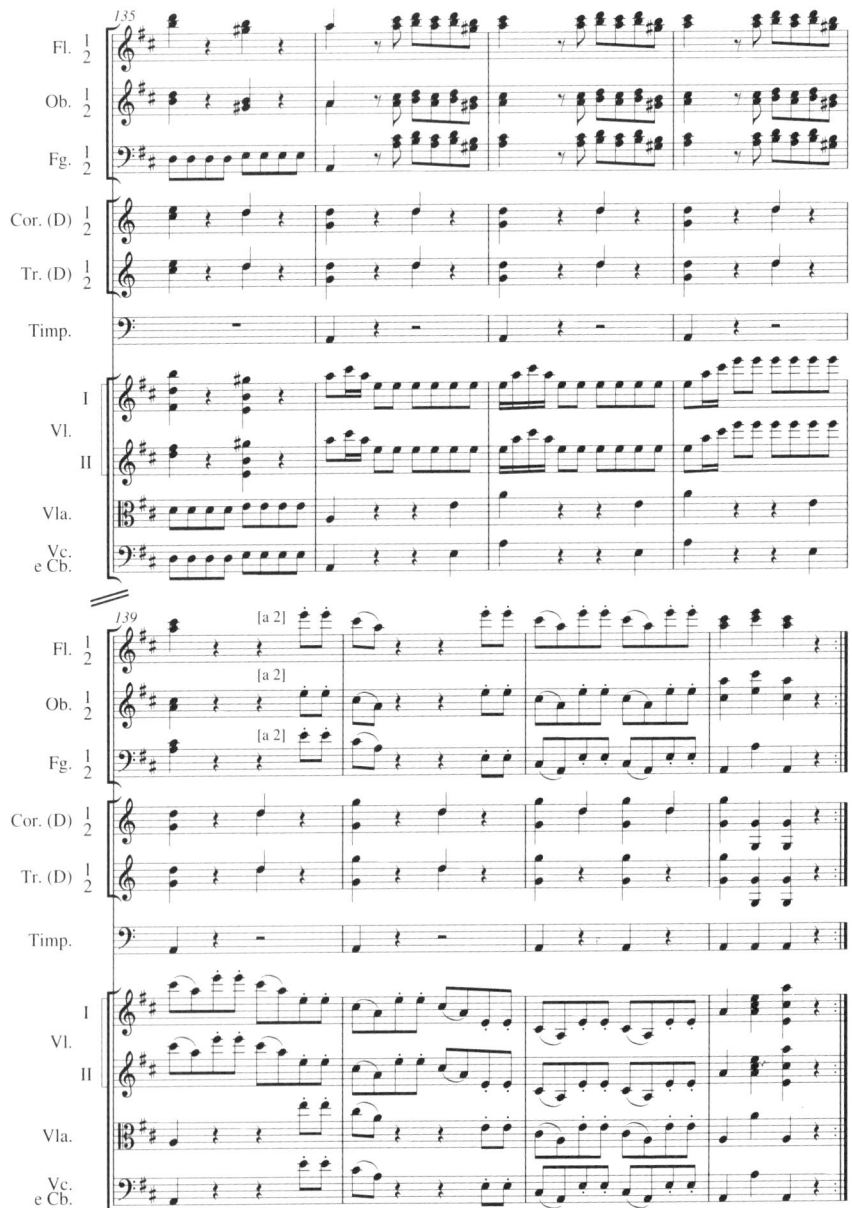

28

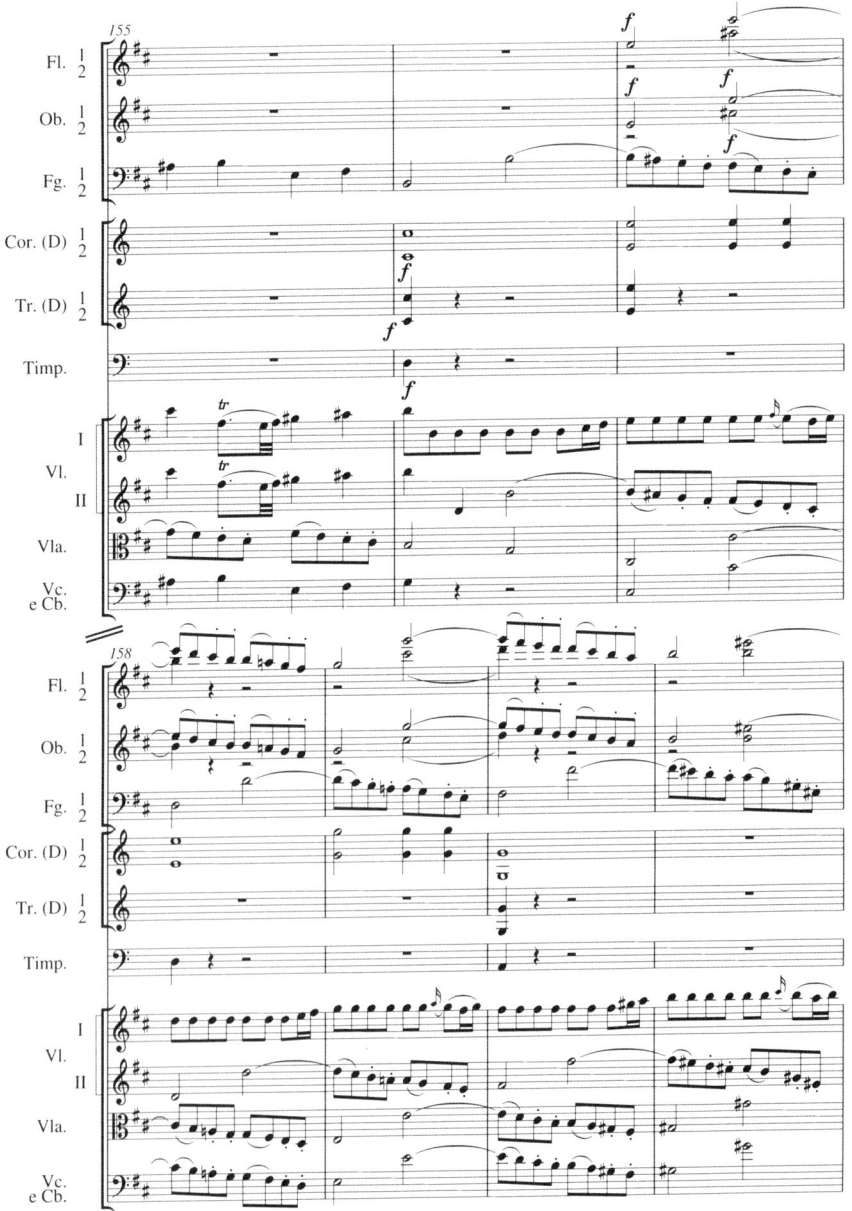

30

EE 7092

32

34

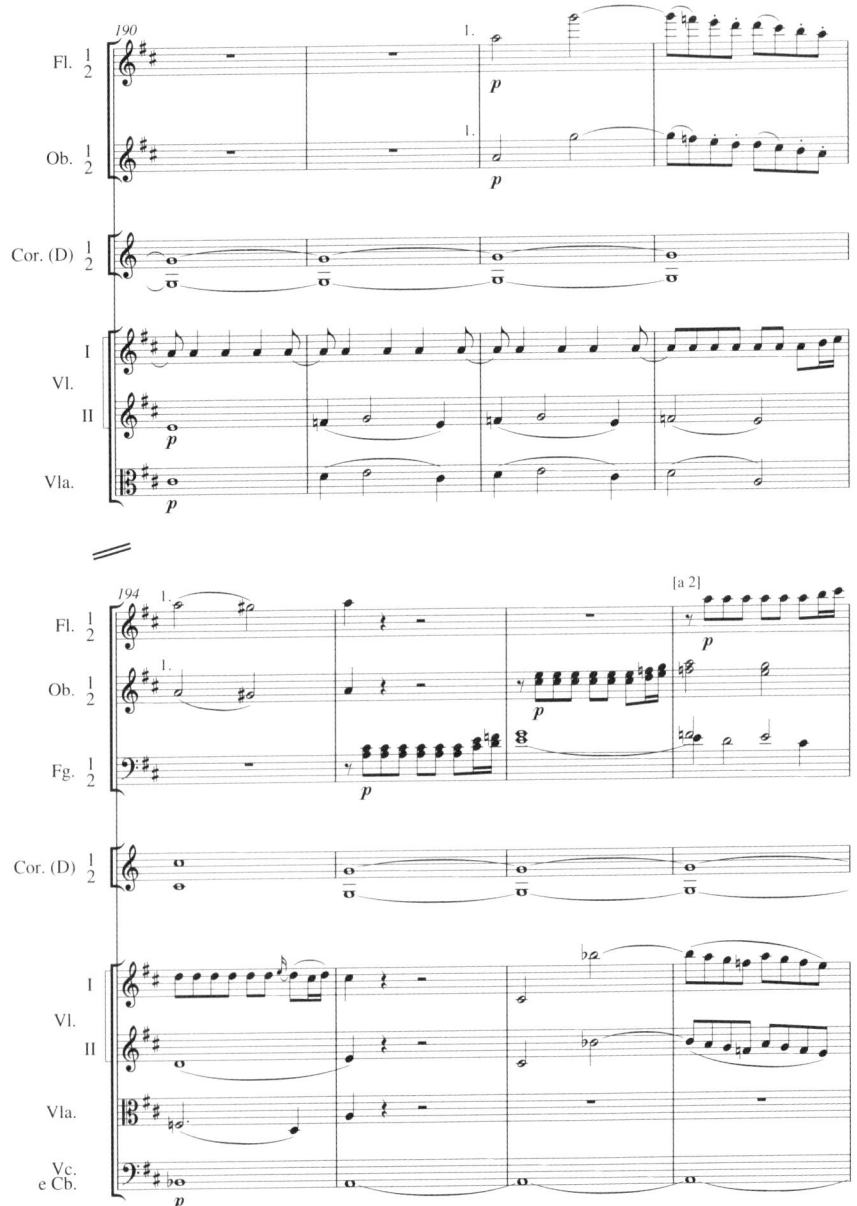

EE 7092

36

38

40

44

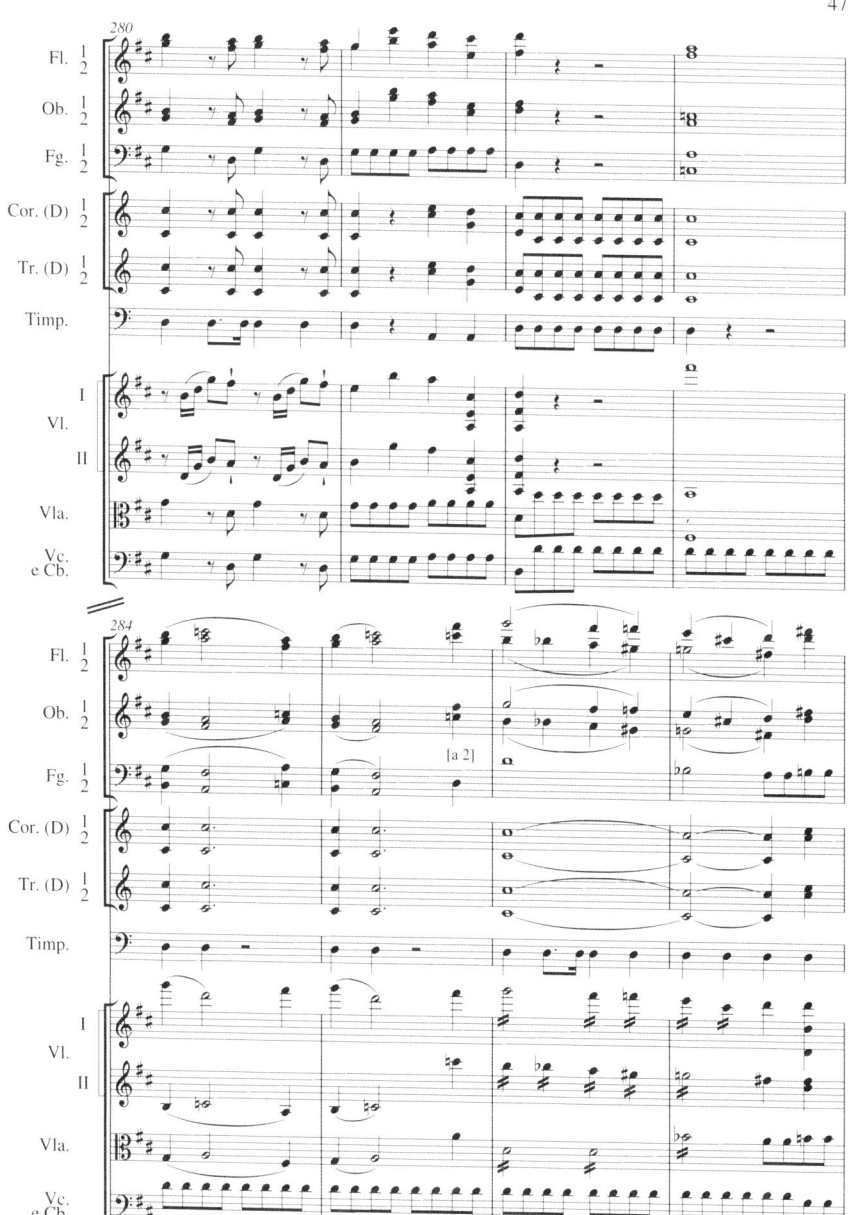

48

50

II. **Andante**

52

56

58

62

EE 7092

64

66

III. **Presto**

70

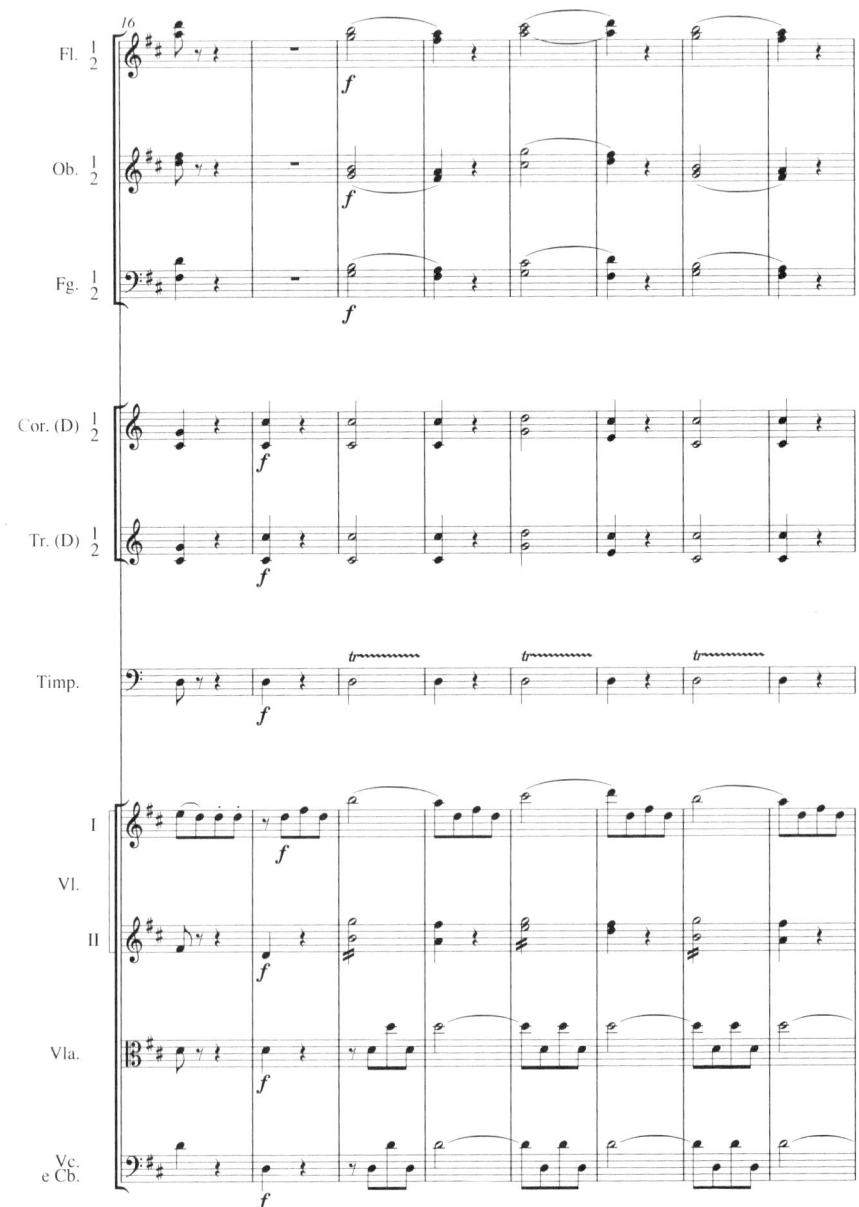

EE 7092

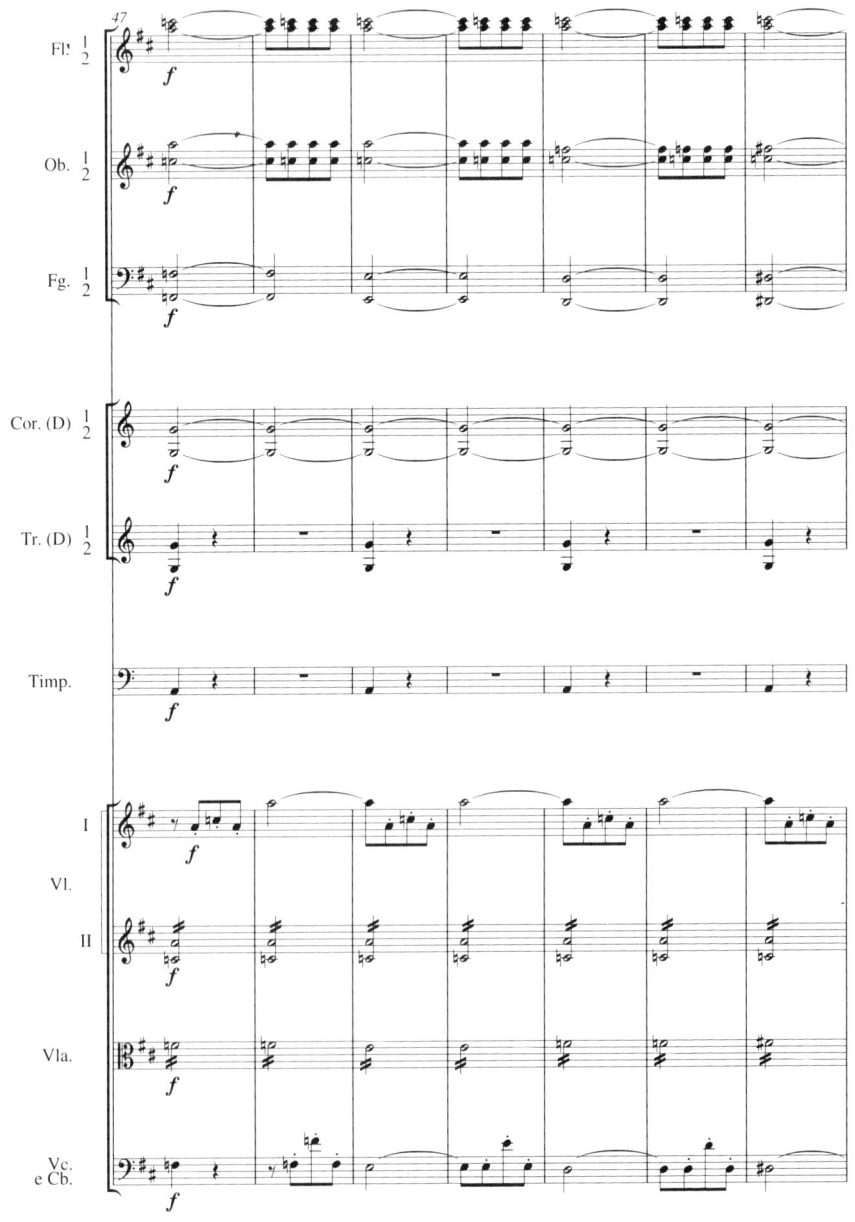

74

78

EE 7092

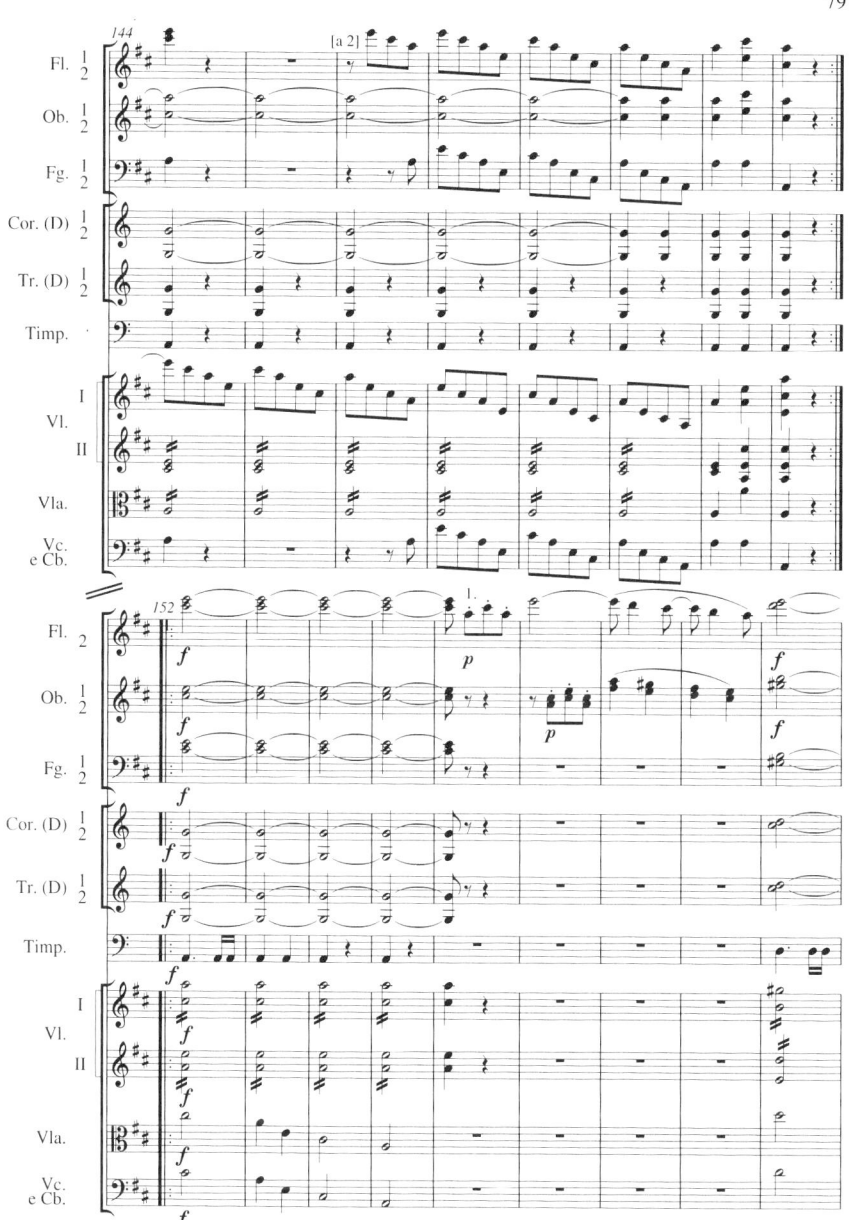

80

82

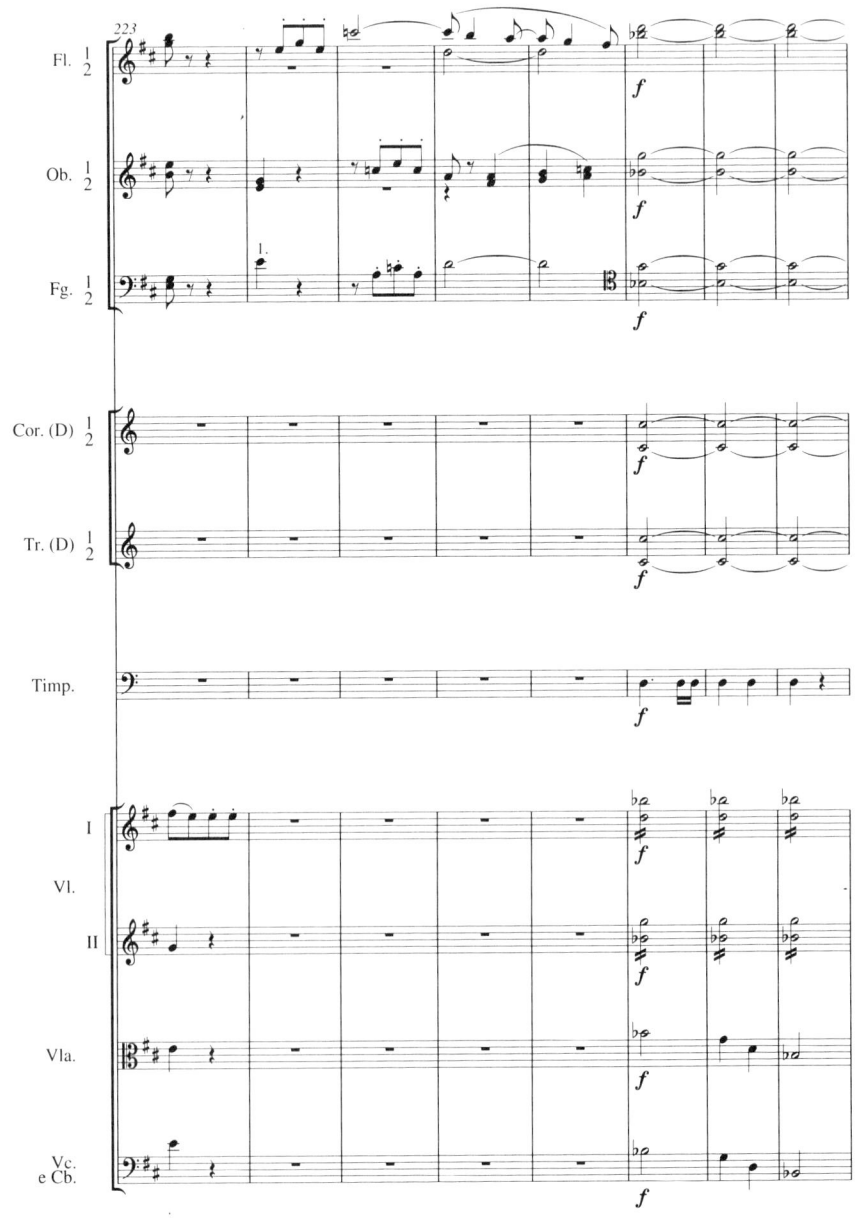

85

EE 7092

88

92

94

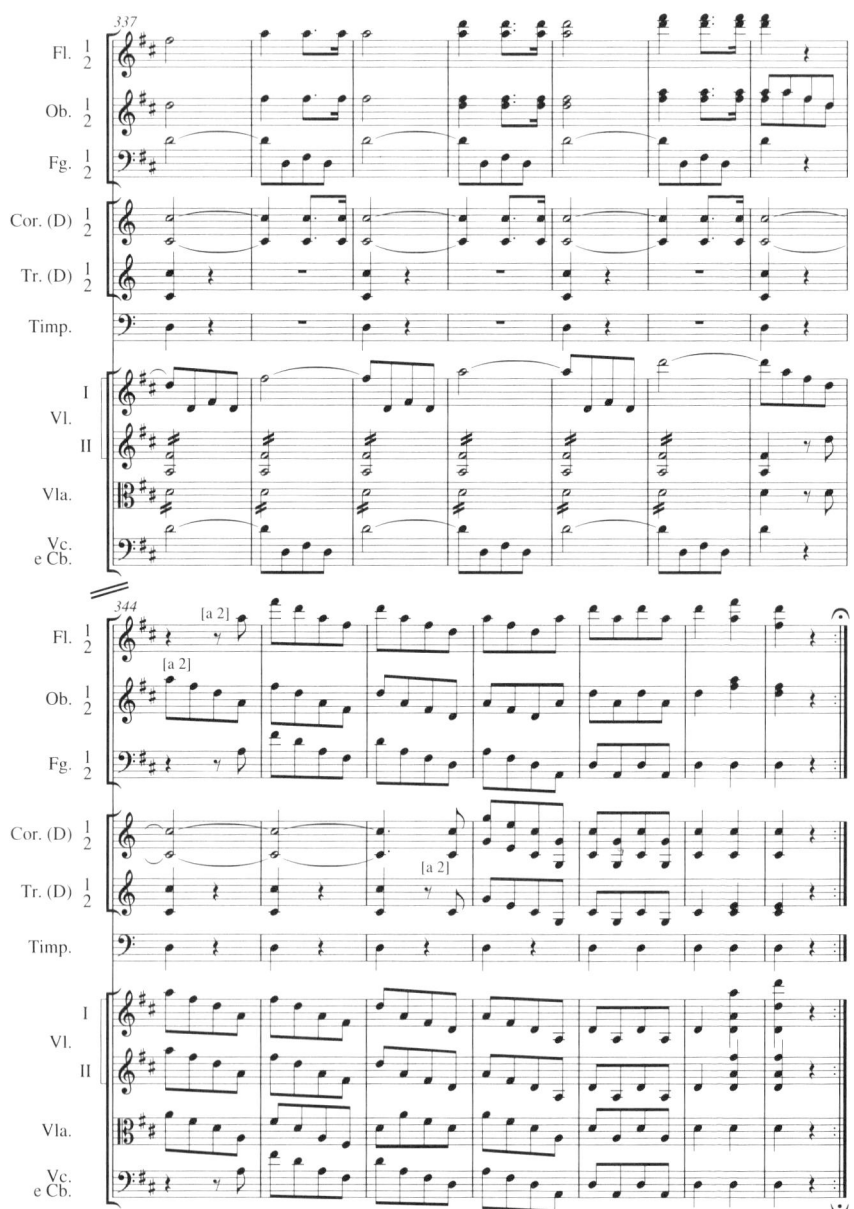